THE

BEATLES

GOLD

Published by:
Wise Publications,
14-15 Berners Street, London W1T 3LJ, UK.

Exclusive Distributors:
Music Sales Limited,
Distribution Centre, Newmarket Road, Bury St Edmunds, Suffolk IP33 3YB, UK.
Music Sales Pty Limited,
Units 3-4, 17 Willfox Street, Condell Park, NSW 2200, Australia.

Order No. NO91487
ISBN 978-1-84938-876-4

Edited by Jenni Wheeler.

Printed in the EU.

www.musicsales.com

WISE PUBLICATIONS
part of The Music Sales Group

London / New York / Paris / Sydney / Copenhagen / Berlin / Madrid / Hong Kong / Tokyo

All You Need Is Love

Words & Music by John Lennon & Paul McCartney

G
D/F♯
Em
Noth - ing you can sing that can't be sung.
No one you can save that can't be saved.
Noth - ing you can see that is - n't shown.
D7/A
G
D/F♯
D7/E
Noth - ing you can say but you can learn how to play the game.
Noth - ing you can do but you can learn how to be you in time.
No - where you can be that is - n't where you're meant to be.
It's
D7
D7/C
D7
G
A
eas - y.
All you need is love.
D7
G
A
D7
All you need is love.

G B7 Em G/D C D
To Coda
All you need is love, love. Love is all you need.
G G D/F♯ Em G D/F♯ Em
Love, love, love. Love, love, love.
D7/A G D7/F♯ D9/E D7 D7/C D7 G A
Love, love, love. All you need is love.
D7 G A D7
All you need is love.

G
B7
Em
G/D
3fr
C
D
D.S. al Coda
All you need is love, love.
Love is all you need.
Coda
A
D7
All you need is love.
All you need is love.
All you need is love, love.
Love is all you need.
D7sus
Love is all you need.
Love is
(Love is all you need.)
Repeat and fade

Can't Buy Me Love

Words & Music by John Lennon & Paul McCartney

C
G
— my friend, — if it makes you feel al - right. — 'Cause
— to give, — but what I've got I'll give to you. —
I don't care too

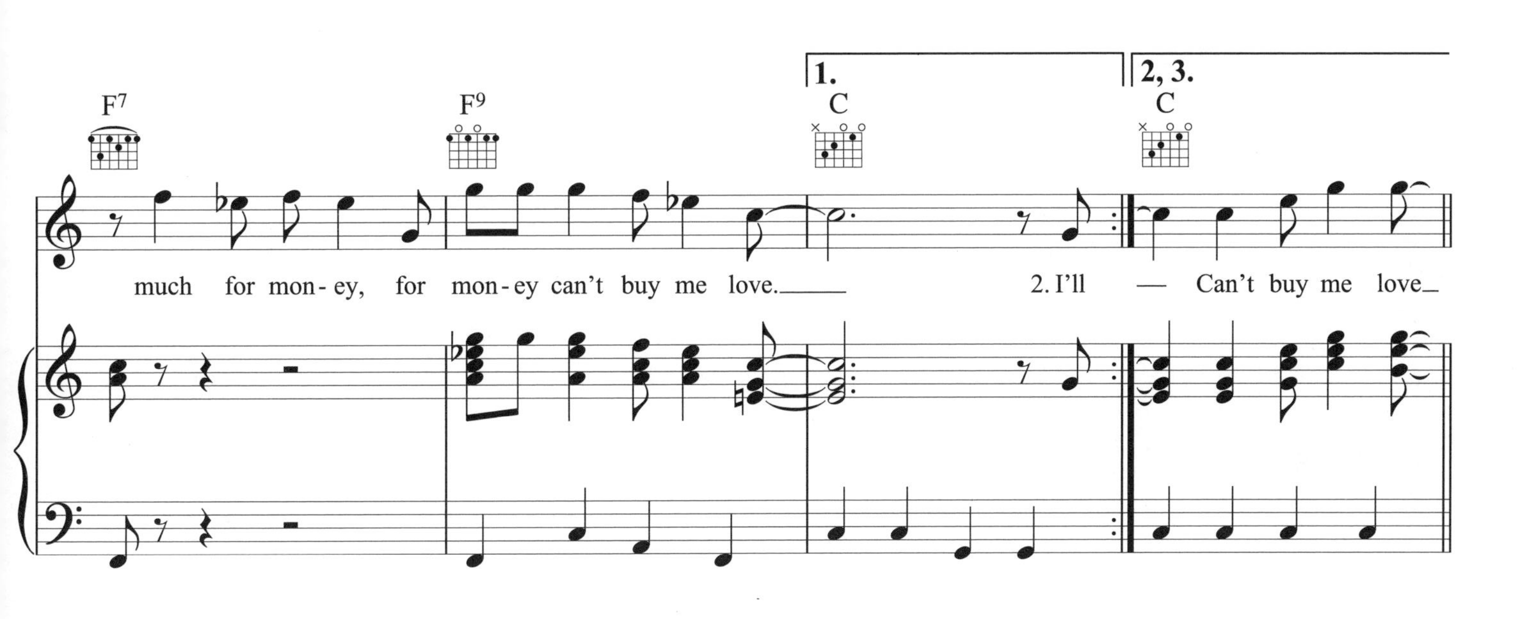
F7
F9
1.
C
2, 3.
C
much for mon - ey, for mon - ey can't buy me love. — 2. I'll
— Can't buy me love —

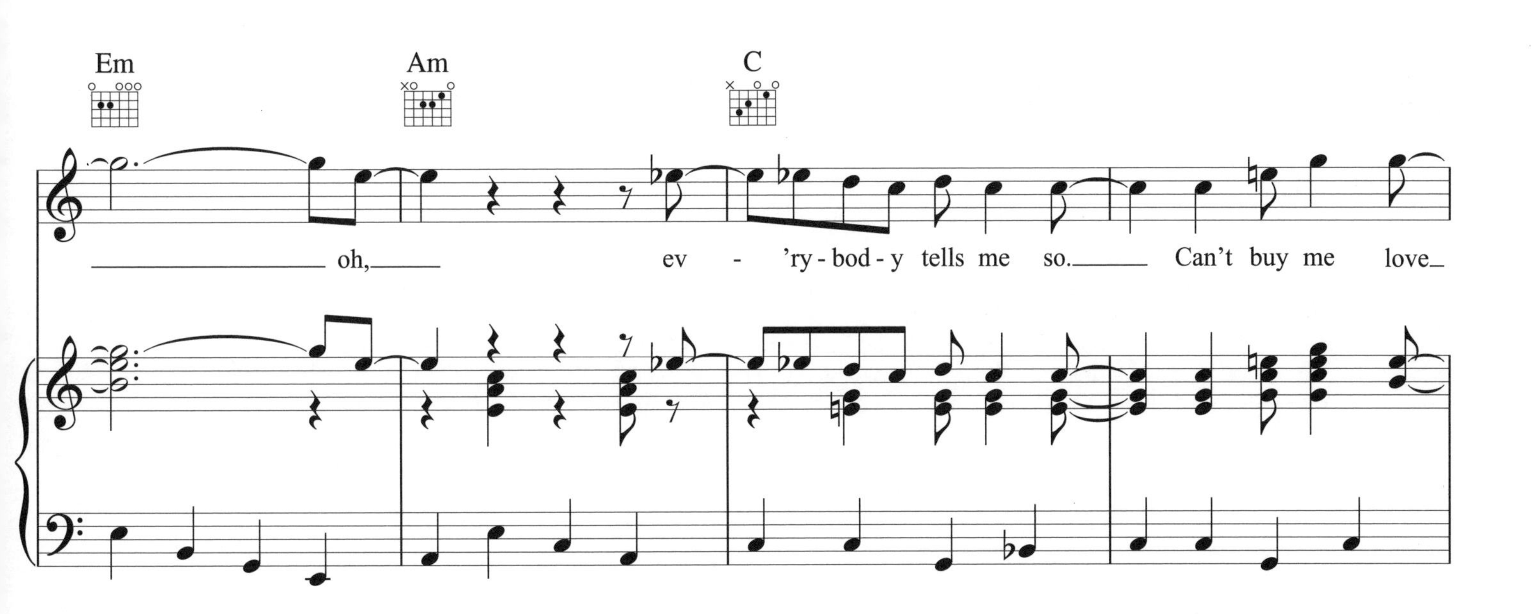
Em
Am
C
— oh, — ev - 'ry - bod - y tells me so. — Can't buy me love —

Em
Am
Dm7
G
C
oh,
no no no,
no!
Say
you don't need no

F7
dia - mond rings
and I'll be sat - is - fied.
Tell
me that you want the kind

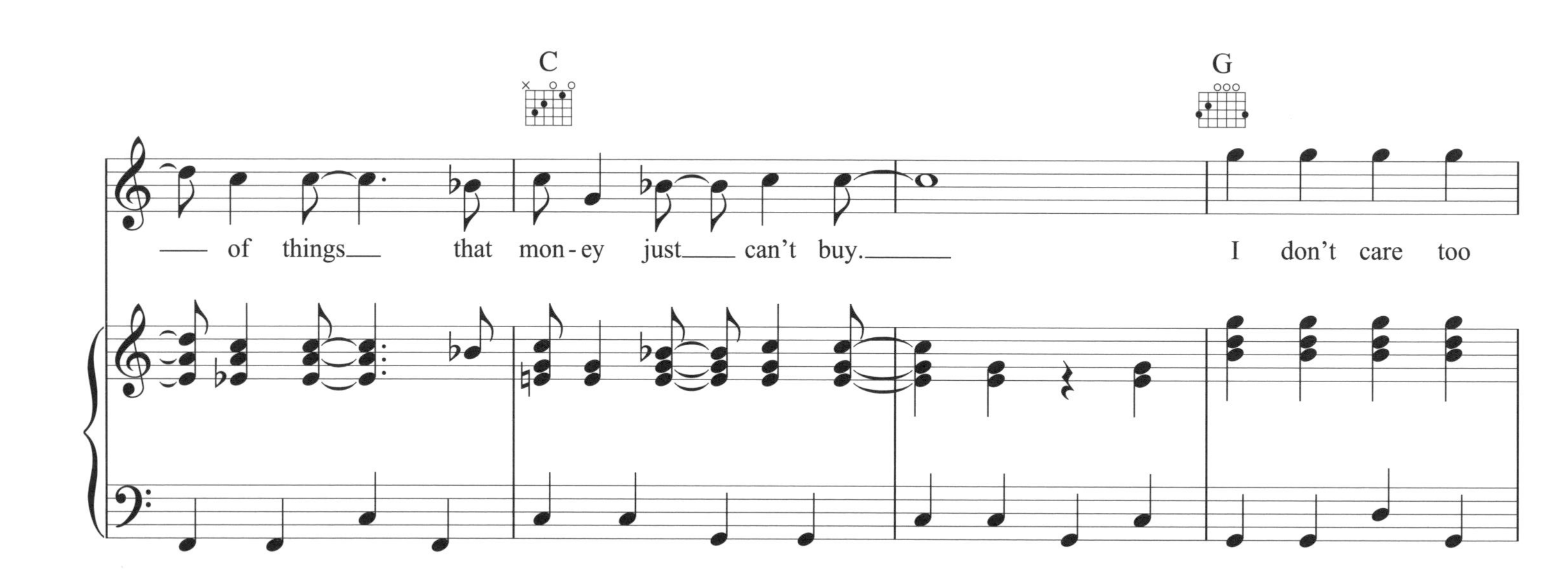
C
G
of things
that mon - ey just can't buy.
I don't care too

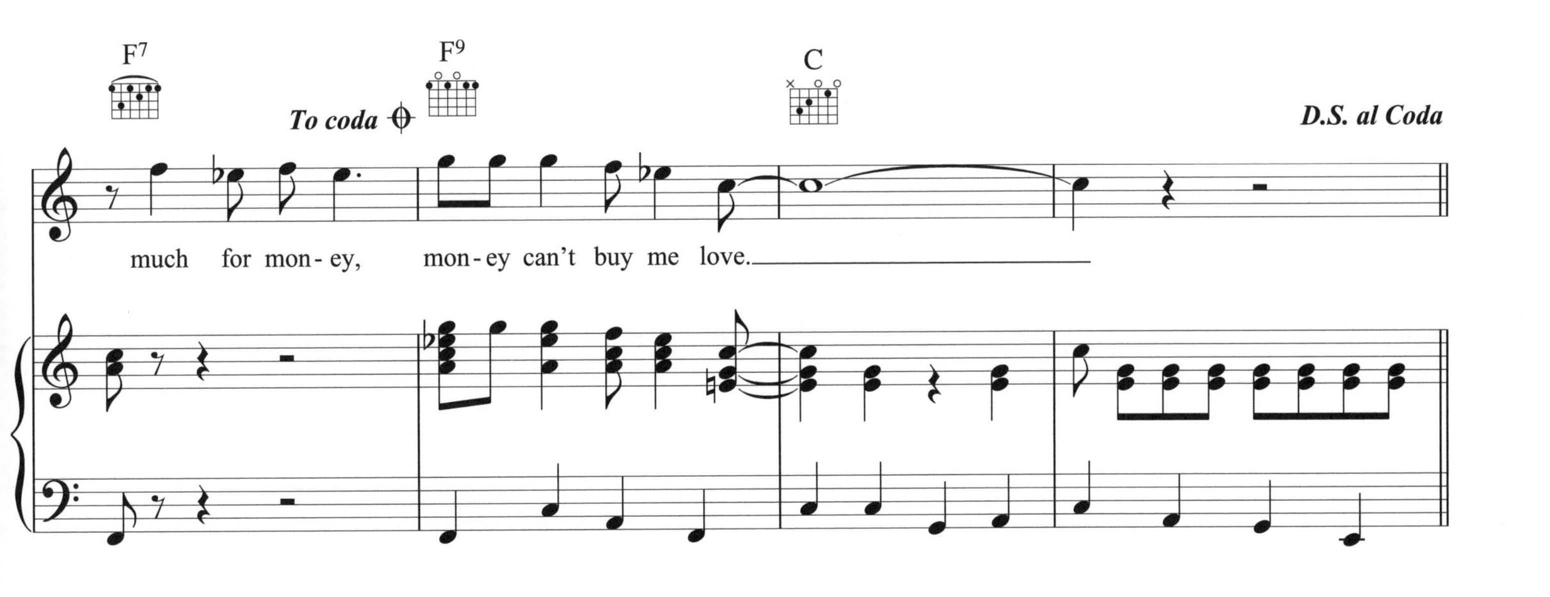
F7
F9
C
To coda
D.S. al Coda
much for mon-ey, mon-ey can't buy me love.

Coda
F7
C
Em
Am
Em
mon-ey can't buy me love. Can't buy me love, love,

Am
Dm7
G13
C
can't buy me love.

Day Tripper

Words & Music by John Lennon & Paul McCartney

A
taking the eas - y way out.
she took me half the way there.
she on - ly played one night stands.
Got a good rea - son
She's a big teas - er,
Tried to please her,
E
for taking the eas - y way out, now. She was a
she took me half the way there, now. She was a
she on - ly played one night stands, now. She was a
F♯
Day Trip - per, one - way tick - et, yeah.
Day Trip - per, one - way tick - et, yeah.
Day Trip - per, Sun - day driv - er, yeah.

A7
G♯7
4fr
It took me so long to find out
C♯
4fr
To Coda
1.
B
2.
B
and I found out.
out.

B7
E
F♯m
G♯m
4fr
Ah.
cresc.
A7
B
D.S. al Coda
Coda
B
out.
play 4 times
E7
Day Trip - per.
Repeat and fade
Day Trip - per, yeah!

Eight Days A Week

Words & Music by John Lennon & Paul McCartney

Bm
G
Bm
E7
Hold me, love me, hold me, love me. I
D
E7
G
D
ain't got nothin' but love, girl, eight days a week.
A
Em
Eight days a week, I love you.
E
G
A
Eight days a week, is not e - nough to show I care.

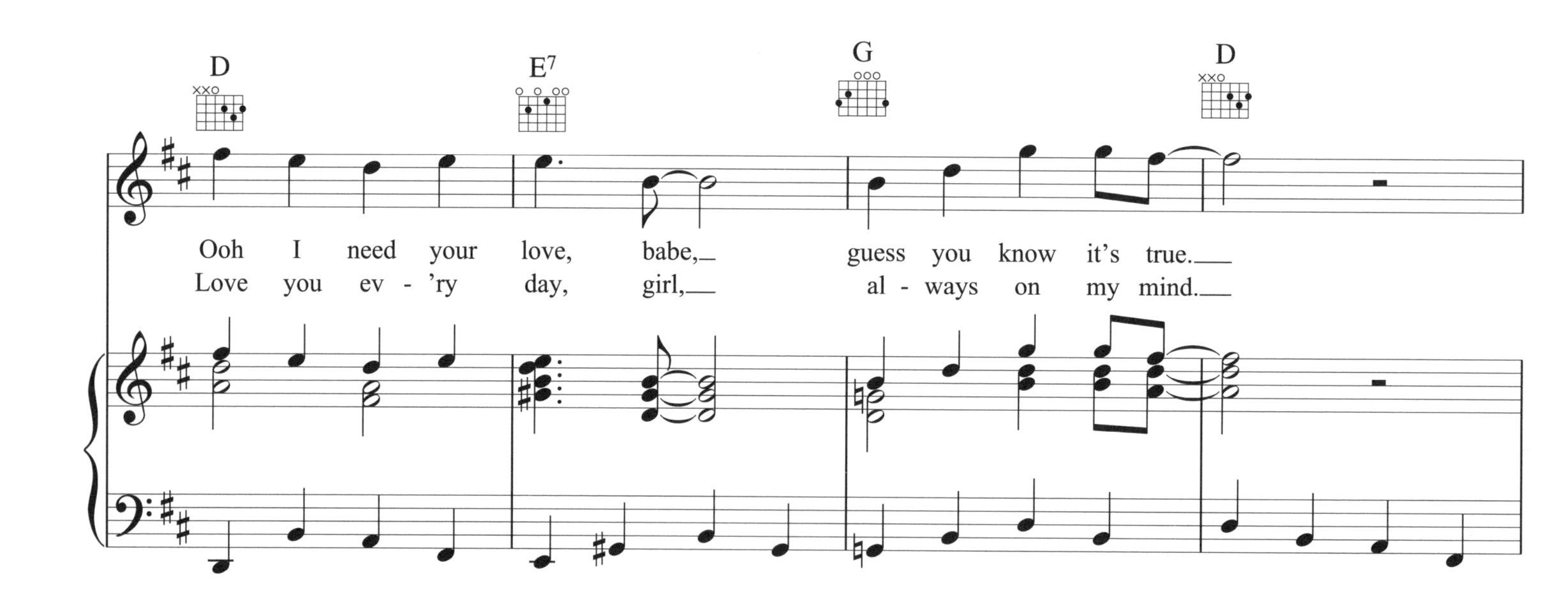
D
E7
G
D
Ooh I need your love, babe,
guess you know it's true.
Love you ev - 'ry day, girl,
al - ways on my mind.

E7
G
D
Hope you need my love, babe,
just like I need you.
One thing I can say, girl,
love you all the time.

Bm
G
Bm
E7
Hold me, love me, hold me, love me. I

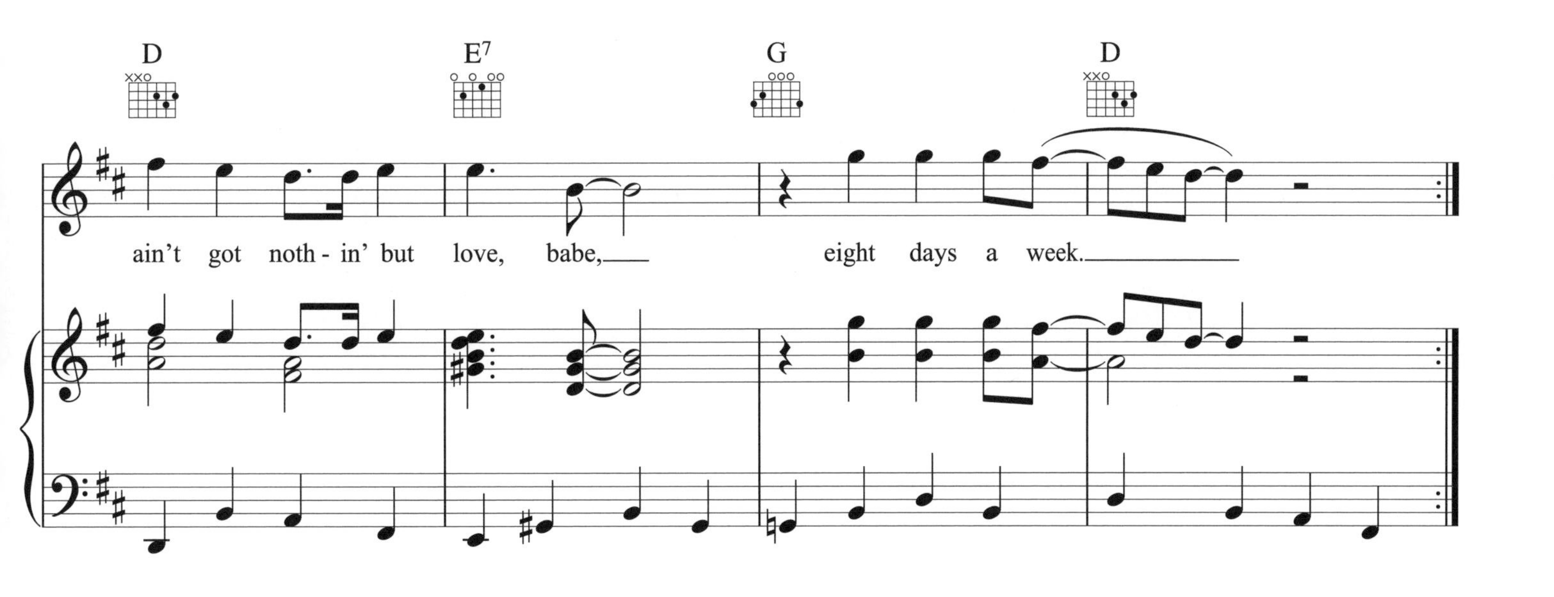
D
E7
G
D
ain't got noth - in' but love, babe,
eight days a week.

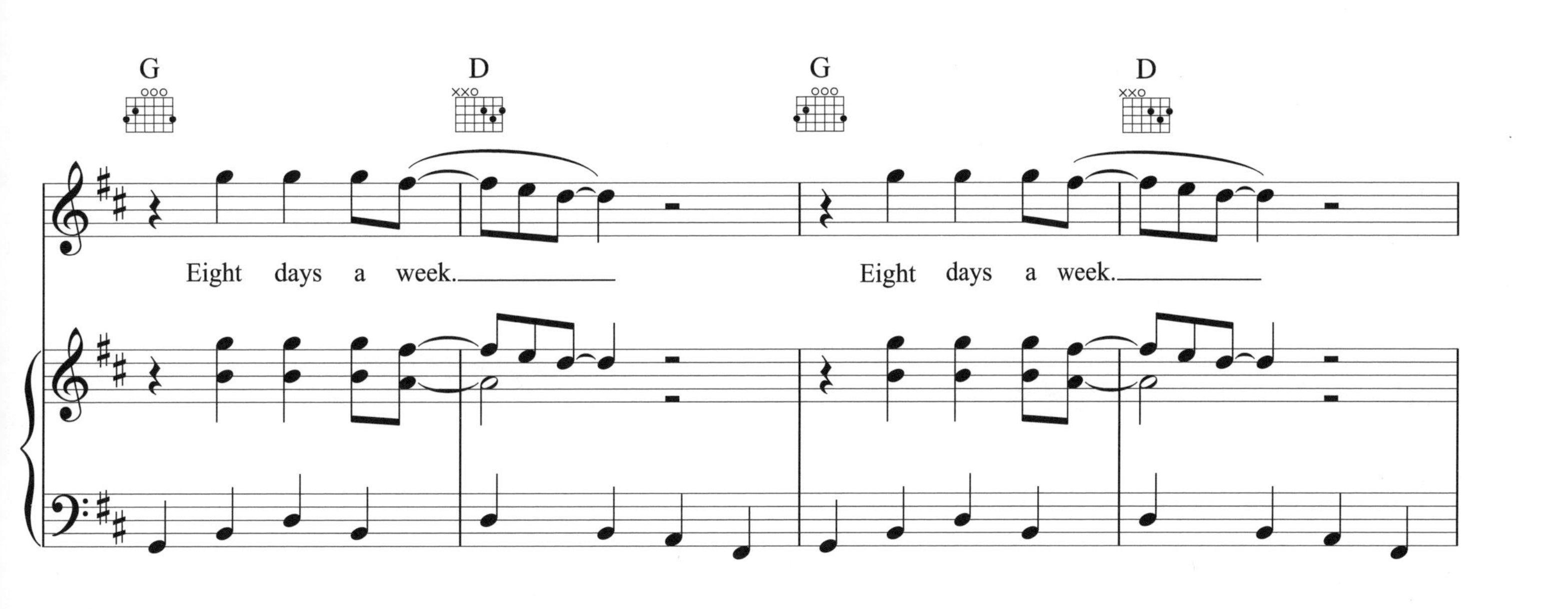
G
D
G
D
Eight days a week.
Eight days a week.

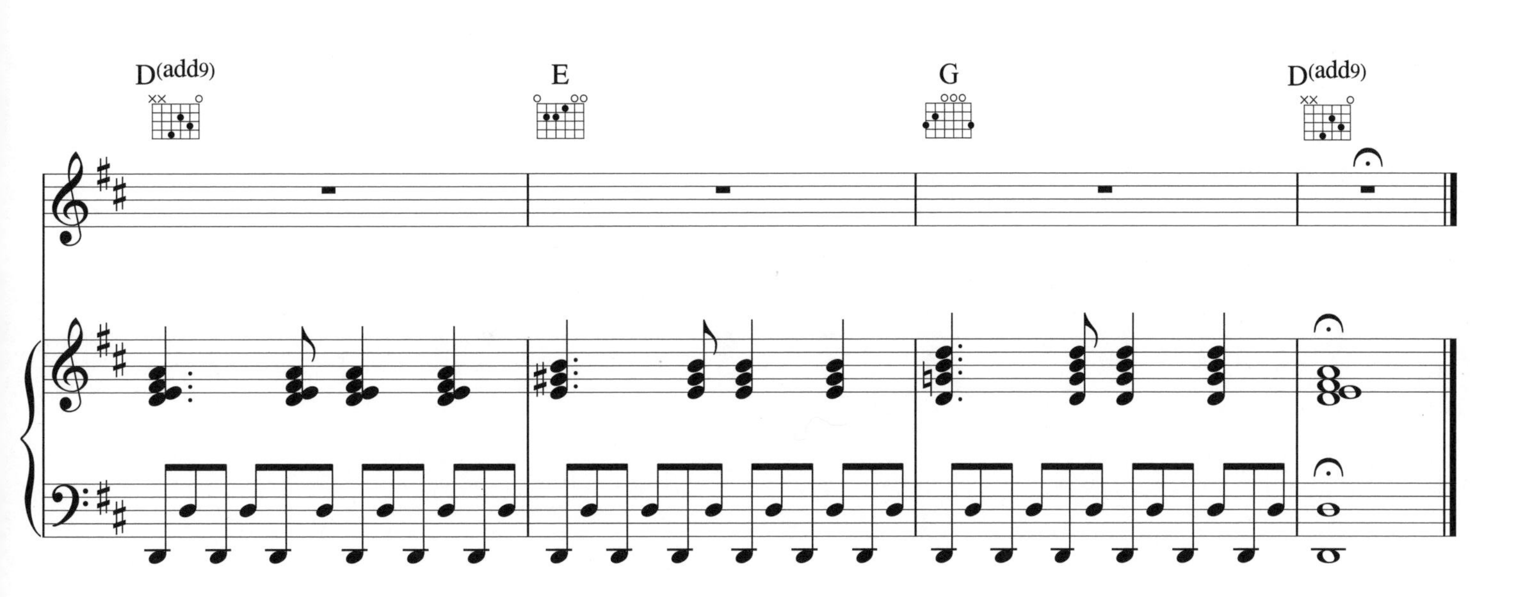
D(add9)
E
G
D(add9)

Eleanor Rigby

Words & Music by John Lennon & Paul McCartney

picks up the rice in the church where a wed - ding has been,
writ - ing the words of a ser - mon that no one will hear,
died in the church and was bur - ied a - long with her name,
C
Em
lives in a dream.
no - one comes near.
no - bod - y came.
Waits at the win - dow,
Look at him work - ing,
Fa - ther Mac - Ken - zie,
wear - ing the face that she keeps in a jar by the door,
darn - ing his socks in the night when there's no - bod - y there,
wip - ing the dirt from his hands as he walks from the grave,
C
Em
Em7
who is it for?
what does he care?
no - one was saved.
All the lone - ly peo -

Em6
C/E
ple, where do they all come from?
Em
Em7
Em6
All the lone - ly peo - ple, where do
1.
2.
C/E
To Coda
Em
Em
D.C. al Coda
they all be - long?
Coda
Em

Get Back

Words & Music by John Lennon & Paul McCartney

♩= 124
A
G D
A A6 A A6 A A6 A A6 D D6 D D6
1. Jo Jo was a man who thought_ he was a lon - er, but___ he knew it could - n't last.__
2. Sweet Lor - et - ta Mar - tin thought_ she was a wo - man, but___ she was an - oth - er man._
A A A6 A A6 A A6 A A6
Jo Jo left his home in Tuc - son Ar - i - zo - na for__
All the girls a - round her say___ she's got it com - ing but__

D D6 D D6 A A7
some Cal - i - for - nia grass.
she gets it while she can.
Get back,
get back,
D7 A7 G D A7
get back to where you once be - longed.
Get back,
get back,
D7 A7
get back to where you once be - longed.
(Spoken) Get back Jo Jo
2º Loretta.
A D7 A G D

A
D7
To Coda
A G D
(1º only) Go home.
Get back,
A7
D D6 D D6
A A6 G D
get back,
back to where you once be-longed.
Get back,
A A7 A A7
A A6 A D
get back,
back to where you once be-longed.
A
Get back Jo.

D7
A7
D.S. al Coda
D7
A7
G
D
Coda
A7
Go home. Oh get back, yeah get back, get back
D7
A7
G
D
A
A7
to where you once be - longed. Yeah get back, get back,

A
A7
D7
get back to where you once be - longed.
A
G
D
(Spoken) Get back, Loretta, your mommy's waiting for you
wearing her high-heeled shoes
and low
necked sweater. Get back home, Loretta.
G
D
A7
Get back,
get back,
oh, get back
G
D
A7
Repeat and fade
to where you once be-longed.
Oh, get back,
get back
back

Hey Jude

Words & Music by John Lennon & Paul McCartney

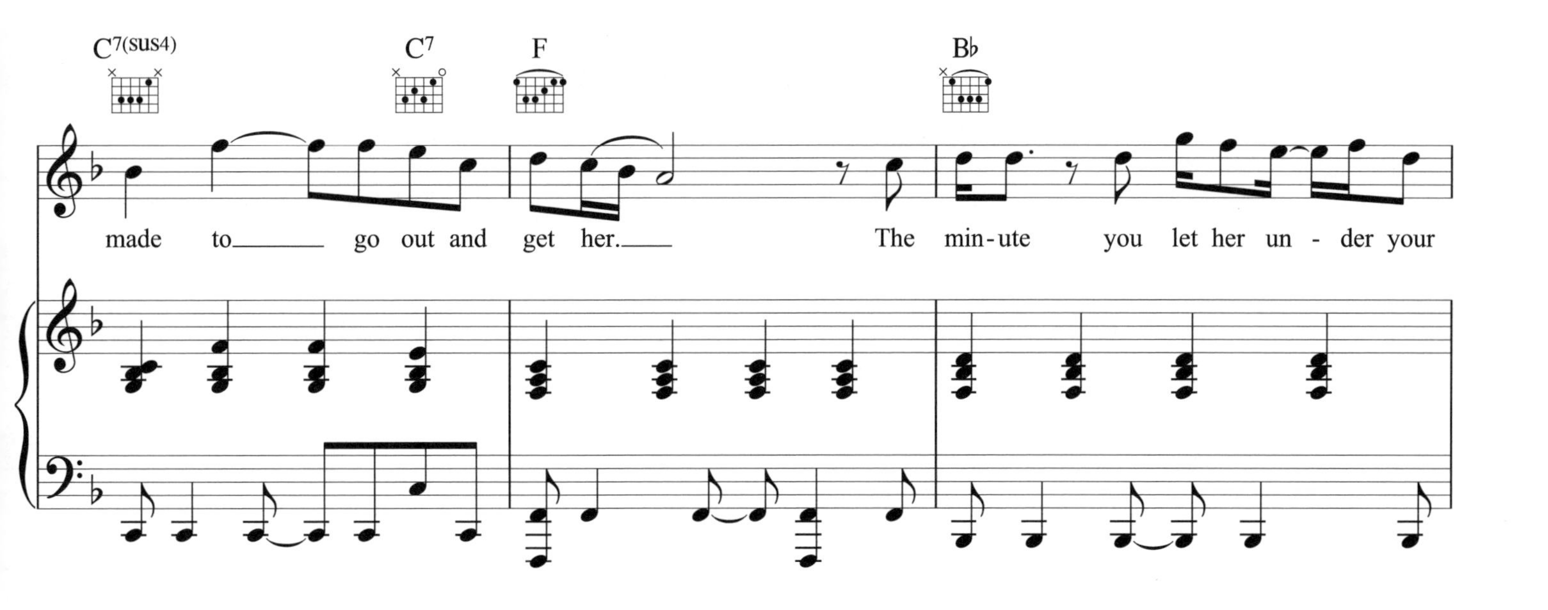
C7(sus4)
C7
F
B♭
made to go out and get her. The min-ute you let her un - der your

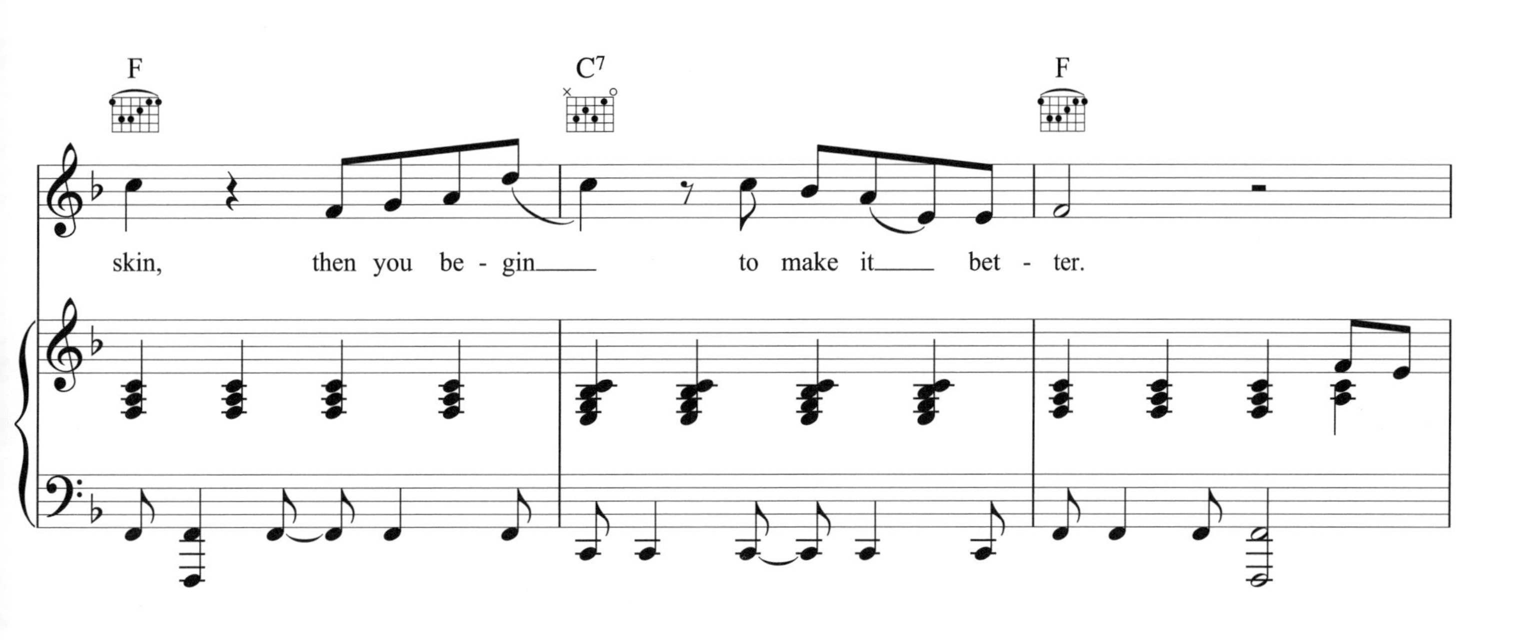
F
C7
F
skin, then you be - gin to make it bet - ter.

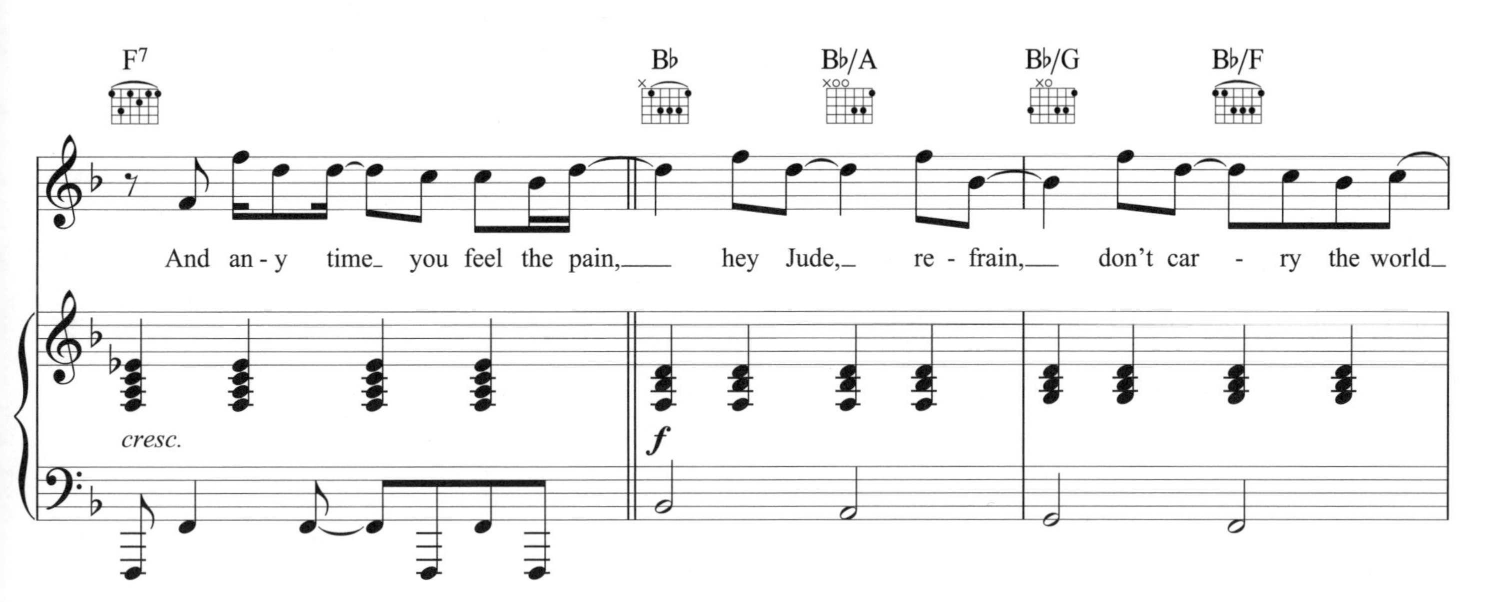
F7
B♭
B♭/A
B♭/G
B♭/F
And an-y time you feel the pain, hey Jude, re - frain, don't car - ry the world
cresc.
f

C7/E C7 F F7
up - on your shoul - ders. For well you know that it's a fool
B♭ B♭/A B♭/G B♭/F C7/E C7
who plays it cool by mak - ing his world a lit - tle cold -
F F7 C7
- er. Na na na na na na na na na.
2/4 4/4
3. Hey
F C C7(sus4)
Jude don't let me down, you have found her now go and
mf

F Bb F
get her. Re - mem-ber to let her in - to your heart then you can start
C7 F F7
to make it bet - ter. So let it out and let it in,
Bb Bb/A Bb/G Bb/F C7/E C7
hey Jude, be - gin, you're wait - ing for some - one to per - form
f
F F Bb Bb/A
with. And don't you know that it's just you, hey Jude, you'll do,

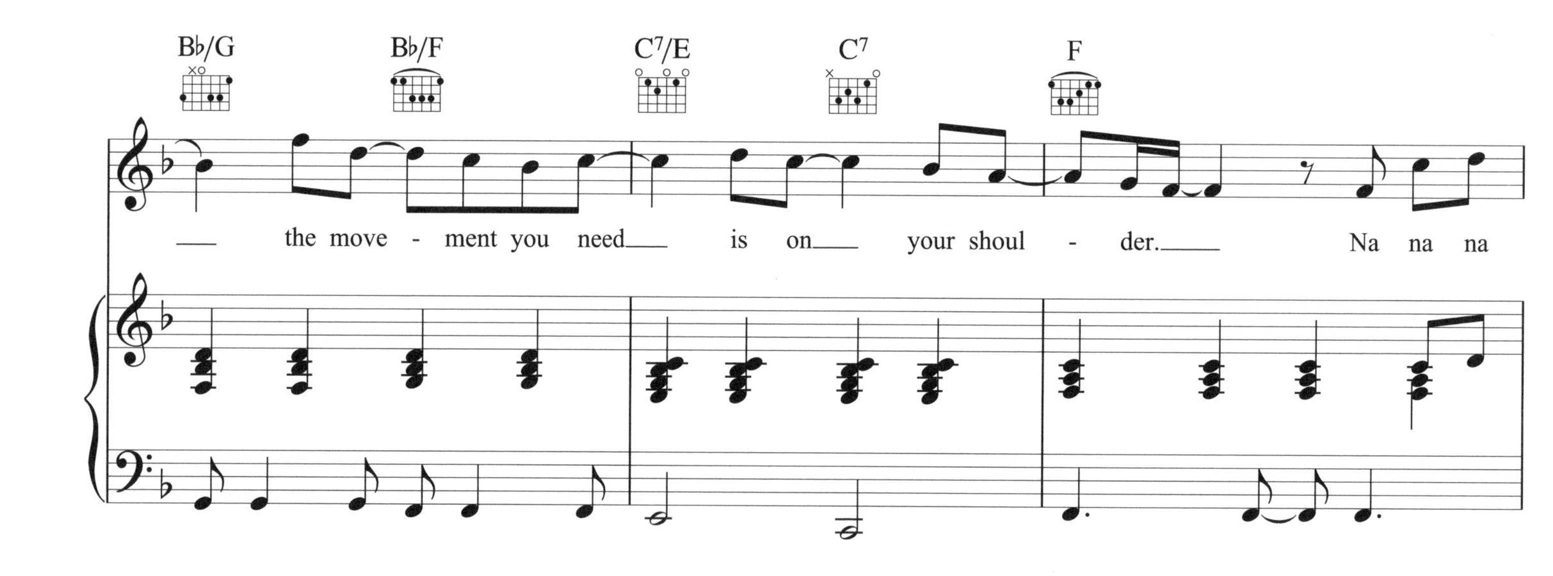
B♭/G B♭/F C7/E C7 F
the move - ment you need is on your shoul - der. Na na na

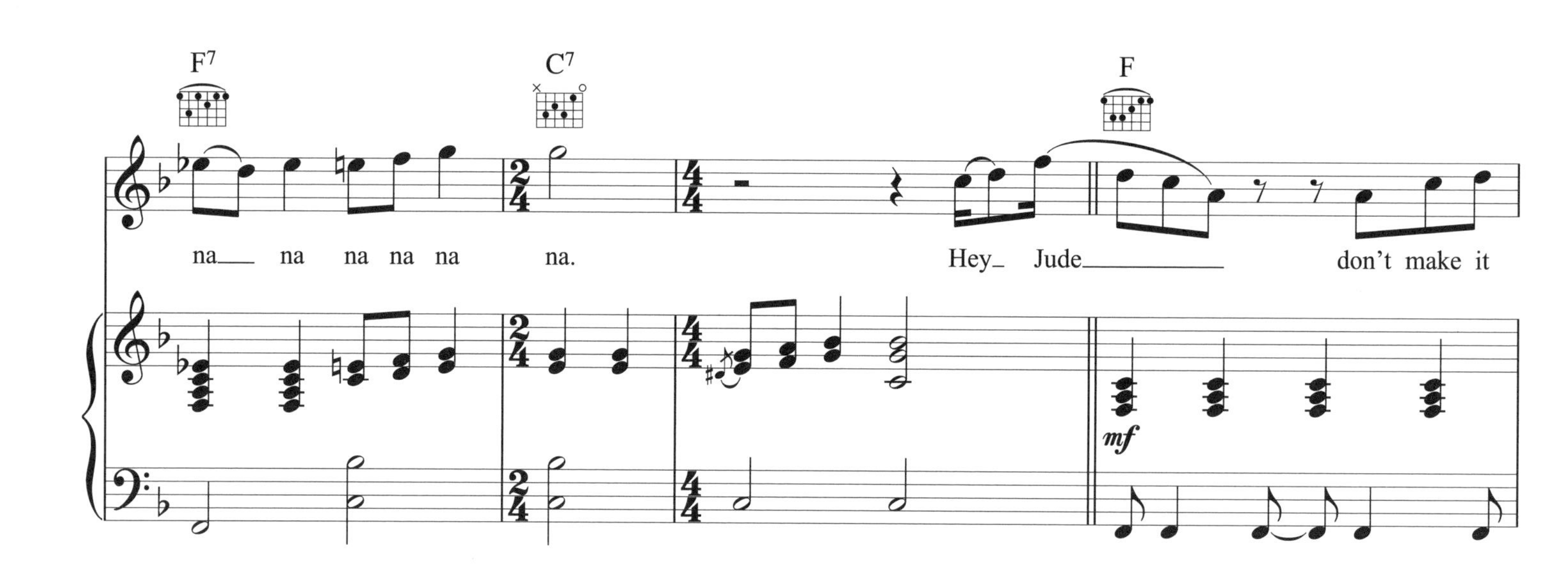
F7 C7 F
na na na na na na. Hey Jude don't make it
mf

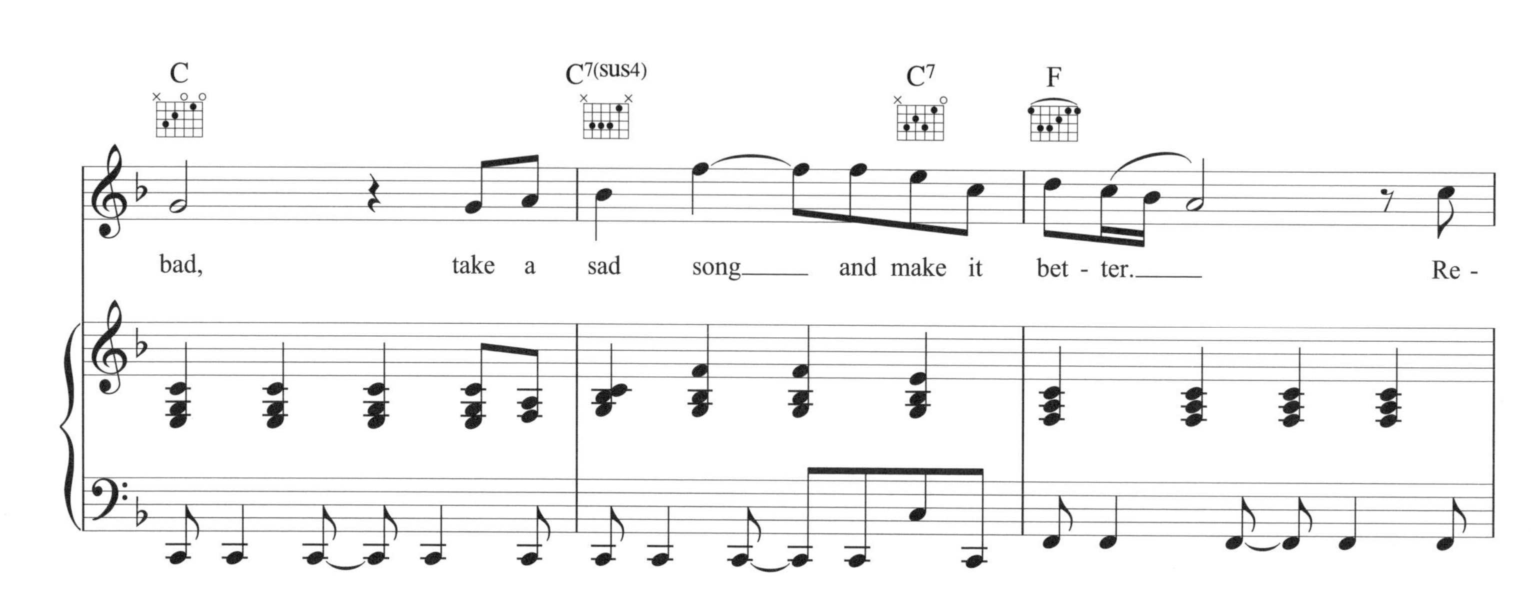
C C7(sus4) C7 F
bad, take a sad song and make it bet - ter. Re -

B♭
F
C7
-mem - ber to let her un - der your skin then you be - gin to make it bet -

F
F
- ter, bet - ter, bet - ter, bet - ter, bet - ter, bet - ter, oh! Na na na
cresc.
f

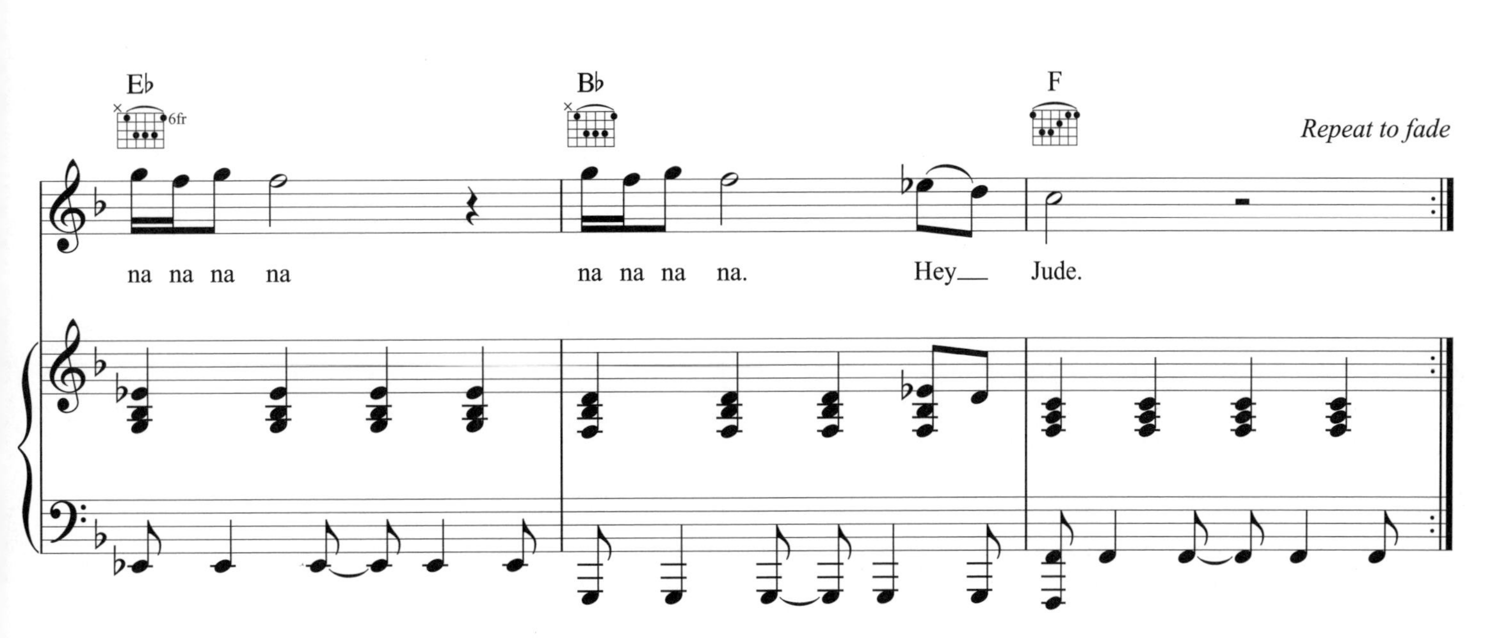
E♭
6fr
B♭
F
Repeat to fade
na na na na na na na na. Hey Jude.

Help!

Words & Music by John Lennon & Paul McCartney

F#m
D
G
I nev - er need - ed an - y - bod - y's help in an - y way.
my in - de - pen - dence seems to van - ish in the haze.
A
C#m
4fr
But now these days are gone, I'm not so self - as - sured,
But ev - 'ry now and then I feel so in - se - cure,
F#m
now I find I've changed my mind, I've
I know that I just need you like I've
D
G
A
Bm
o - pened up the doors.
nev - er done be - fore.
Help me if you can, I'm feel - ing

Bm/A
G
down,
and I do
ap - pre - ci - ate
you be - ing 'round
E7
Help me get
my feet
back on the ground.
A
N.C.
Won't you please,
please
help
me?
1.
2.
A
F♯m
A
A6
Help me, help me!
Ooh.

In My Life

Words & Music by John Lennon & Paul McCartney

D
Dm
A
F#m7
gone and some re - main. All these (1.) plac - es had their
think of love as some - thing new. Though I (2, 3.) know I'll nev - er lose af -
D
G
A
mo - ments with lov - ers and friends I still can re - call. Some are
- fec - tion for peo - ple and things that went be - fore. I
Fm
B7
Dm
dead and some are liv - ing; in my life I've
know I'll of - ten stop and think a - bout them, in my life I

A
To Coda
A
E
F♯m
A7
loved them all.
love you more.
D
Dm
1.
A
2.
A
D.S. al Coda
Coda
A
E
Slower
Dm
In my life I
a tempo
N.C.
A
E
E7
A
love you more.

Let It Be

Words & Music by John Lennon & Paul McCartney

G
Am
Fmaj7
F6
in my hour of dark - ness, she is stand - ing right in front of me,
C
G
F
C/E
Dm7
C
speak - ing words of wis - dom let it be.
Let it be,
Am
C/G
F
C
G
let it be, let it be, let it be.
Whis - per words of wis - dom, let it be.
F
C/E
Dm7
C
C
G
2. And when the bro - ken heart - ed peo - ple
(3.) when the night is cloud - y there is
mf

Am
Fmaj7
F6
C
G
liv - ing in the world a - gree, there will be an ans - wer let it be.
still a light that shines on me, shine un - til to - mor - row let it be.
F
C/E
Dm7
C
G
For though they may be part - ed there is
I wake up to the sound of mu - sic
Am
Fmaj7
F6
C
G
still a chance that they will see, there will be an ans - wer let it be.
Moth-er Mar - y comes to me, speak - ing words of wis - dom let it be.
F
C/E
Dm7
C
Am
C/G
F
C
Let it be, let it be, let it be, let it be.
f

G
F
C/E
Dm7
C
To Coda
There will be an ans - wer, let it be.
Oh, let it be,
Am
C/G
F
C
let it be,
let it be,
let it be.
C
G
F
C/E
Dm7
C
Whis - per words of wis - dom, let it be.
F
C/E
Dm
C
B♭
F/A
G
F
C
F
C/E
Dm
C
B♭
F/A

G F C G Am Fmaj7 F6
Guitar Solo
C G F C/E Dm7 C G
Am Fmaj7 F6 C G F C/E Dm C G/B
Let it be,
Am C/G F C
let it be, let it be, yeah, let it be.

C
G
F
C/E
Dm7
C
D.S. al Coda
Whis - per words of wis - dom, let it be.
3. And
Coda
Am
C/G
F
C
let it be, let it be, yeah let it be.
C
G
F
C/E
Dm7
C
Whis - per words of wis - dom, let it be.
rall.
F
C/E
Dm
C
B♭
F/A
G
F
C

Lucy In The Sky With Diamonds

Words & Music by John Lennon & Paul McCartney

A/G
F♯m7
Dm
A/E
calls you, you an - swer quite slow - ly, a girl with ka -
smile as you drift past the flow - ers that grow so in -
some - one is there at the turn - stile, the girl with ka -
A/G
To Coda
F♯m7
Dm
Dm/C
- lei - do - scope eyes.
- cred - ib - ly high.
- lei - do - scope
B♭
C9
Cel - lo - phane flow - ers of yel - low and green,
News - pa - per tax - is ap - pear on the shore,
F
B♭
C9
tow - er - ing o - ver your head.
wait - ing to take you a - way.
Look for the
Climb in the

G
D7
Em
(𝅗𝅥. = ♩) poco accel.
girl with the sun in her eyes and she's gone.
back with your head in the clouds and you're gone.
G
C
D7
G
Lu - cy in the sky with dia - monds,
Lu - cy in the sky with dia - monds,
Lu - cy in the sky with dia - monds.
1.
2.
D
D
D.S. al Coda
Ah.
Ah.
Coda
F♯m
eyes.

D
G
C
Lu - cy in the sky with
D7
G
C
dia - monds,
Lu - cy in the sky with
D7
G
C
dia - monds,
Lu - cy in the sky with
D7
G
A
Repeat and fade
dia - monds.
Ah.

Penny Lane

Words & Music by John Lennon & Paul McCartney

F♯sus4
F♯
B
B/A♯
B/G♯
B/F♯
C♯m7
4fr
F♯
On the cor-ner is a ban - ker with a mo - tor car, the lit-tle chil-
2° Instrumental solo till *
B
B/A♯
B/G♯
B/F♯
Bm
G♯m7♭5
- dren laugh at him be-hind his back. And the ban-ker nev - er wears a mac
Gmaj7
F♯sus4
F♯
E
in the pour - ing rain. Very strange. *
Pen-ny Lane
A
A/C♯
D
is in my ears and in my eyes.

A
A/C♯
D
There be - neath the blue sub - ur - ban skies I sit and
A four of fish and fin - ger pies in sum - mer.
1.
2.
F♯
mean - while… 2. Back in Pen - ny Lane
Mean - while... 3. Back be - hind the
B
B/A♯
B/G♯
B/F♯
C♯m7
F♯
shel - ter in the mid - dle of the round - a - bout a pret - ty nurse
Bm
G♯m7♭5
is sell - ing pop - pies from a tray. And though she feels as if she's in a play

Gmaj7 F♯sus4 F♯ F♯sus4 F♯
she is an - y way. Pen-ny Lane
B B/A♯ B/G♯ B/F♯ C♯m7 F♯
4fr
the bar - ber shaves an - oth - er cus - to - mer. We see the
B B/A♯ B/G♯ B/F♯ Bm G♯m7♭5
ban - ker sit - ting wait - ing for a trim. Then the fire - man rush - es in
Gmaj7 F♯sus4 F♯ E
from the pour - ing rain. Ver - y strange. Pen - ny Lane

A
A/C♯
D
is in my ears and in my eyes.
A
A/C♯
D
F♯
There be-neath the blue sub-ur-ban skies I sit and mean-while... Back in Pen-ny Lane
B
B/D♯
E
is in my ears and in my eyes.
B
B/D♯
E
B
There be-neath the blue sub-ur-ban skies. Pen-ny Lane.

Something

Words & Music by George Harrison

♩ = 66
C
Cmaj7
1. Some - thing in the way she moves,
2. Some - where in her smile she knows,
3. Instrumental
4. Some - thing in the way she moves,
C7
F
at - tracts me like no oth - er lov - er;
that I don't need no oth - er lov - er;
and all I have to do is think of her;
D7
G
Am7
G7/B
some - thing in the way she woos me.
some - thing in her style that shows me.
some - thing in the way she shows me.
I

Am
Am(maj7)
Am7/G
D7
To Coda
don't want to leave her now,
you know I be - lieve and how.
1.
2.
F
E♭
G7/D
6fr
A
Double tempo
C♯m/G♯
4fr
F♯m
You're ask - ing me will my love grow;
F♯m/E
D
G
I don't know, I don't

A
C♯m/G♯
4fr
know.
You stick a - round now it may
F♯m
F♯m/E
D
G
show.
I don't know, I don't
D.S. al Coda
Coda
C
F
E♭
6fr
G7
know.
A
F
E♭
6fr
G7/D
C

She Loves You

Words & Music by John Lennon & Paul McCartney

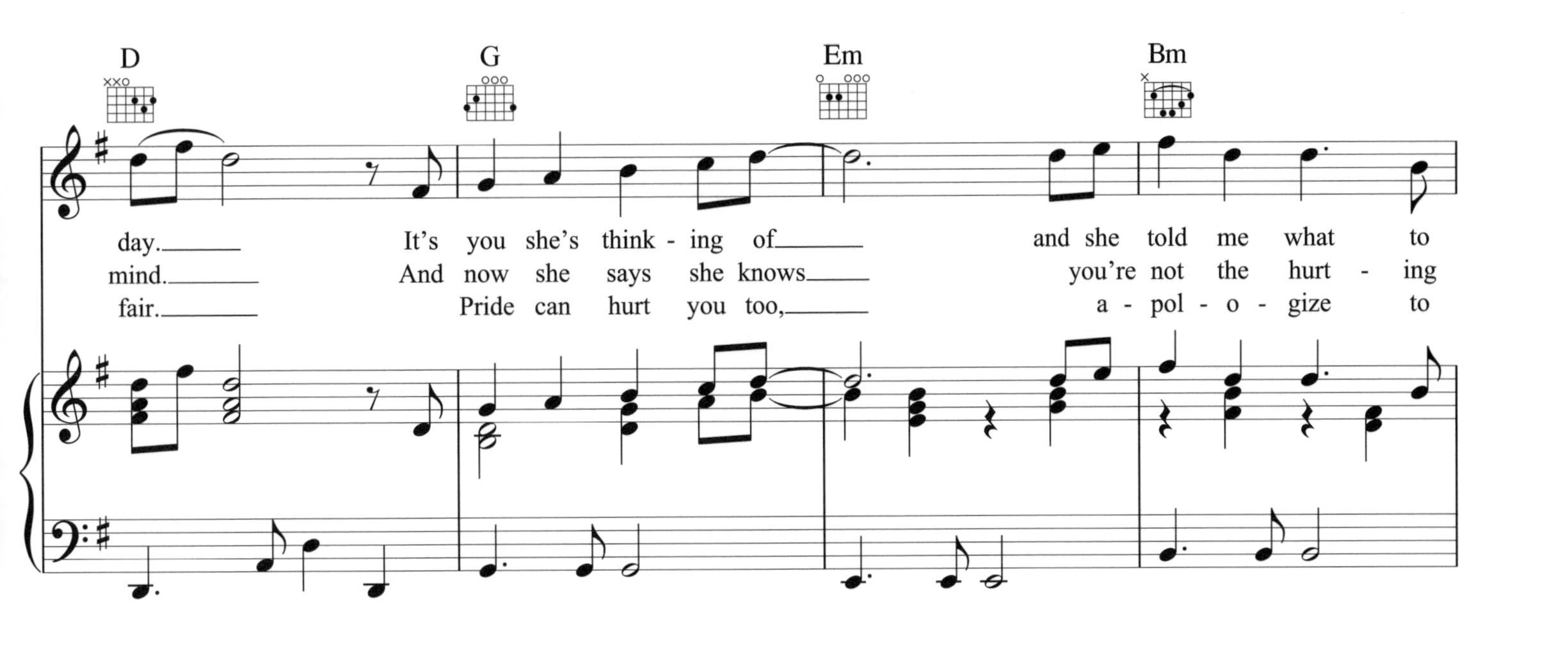
D
G
Em
Bm
day. It's you she's think - ing of and she told me what to
mind. And now she says she knows you're not the hurt - ing
fair. Pride can hurt you too, a - pol - o - gize to

D
G6
say: She says she
kind. She says she
her. Be - cause she
loves you and you know that can't be

Em
Cm6
bad. Yes, she loves you and you know you should be glad.

1.
D7
2. She
2.
D7
Ooh!
She
Em
loves you, yeah, yeah, yeah.
A7
She loves you, yeah,
yeah, yeah. And with a
Cm6
love like that you
Daug
know you
D7
To Coda
should be glad.
G
D.S. al Coda
3. You
Coda
G

Em
Cm6
Daug
D7
With a love like that you know you should be glad.
G
Em
Cm6
With a love like that you
rit.
a tempo
Daug
D7
G
know you should be glad.
Em
C
G6
Yeah, yeah, yeah. Yeah, yeah, yeah, yeah.

Yesterday

Words & Music by John Lennon & Paul McCartney

F5
E7sus4
A7
Dm
Dm/C
2. Sud-den-ly I'm not half the man I used to be.
3. Yes-ter-day love was such an eas-y game to play.
B♭maj7
C7
F
F/E
Dm7
G
There's a shad-ow hang-ing o - ver me. Oh, yes - ter-day came
Now I need a place to hide a-way. Oh, I be-lieve in
B♭
F
Asus4
A7
Dm
C
B♭
Am
sud - den - ly.
yes - ter - day.
Why she had to go, I don't
Gm6
C7
F
Asus4
A7
know. She would - n't say. I said

1.
Dm C B♭ Am Gm6 C7 F
something wrong, now I long for yes - ter - day.
2.
F F5 E7sus4 A7
- day. 4. Yes - ter - day love was such an eas - y
Dm Dm/C B♭maj7 C7 F F/E
game to play. Now I need a place to hide a - way. Oh,
Dm7 G B♭ F F/C rit. G7/B B♭ F
I be - lieve in yes - ter - day. Mm, mm mm mm.
3456789

THE

BEATLES

GOLD

'BONUS CD'
TRACK LISTING

Get Back

(Lennon/McCartney)
Sony/ATV Music Publishing (UK) Limited

Hey Jude

(Lennon/McCartney)
Sony/ATV Music Publishing (UK) Limited

Let It Be

(Lennon/McCartney)
Sony/ATV Music Publishing (UK) Limited